THE ULTIMATE
WOLVERHAMPTON WANDERERS FC TRIVIA BOOK

A Collection of Amazing Trivia Quizzes
and Fun Facts for Die-Hard Wolves Fans!

Ray Walker

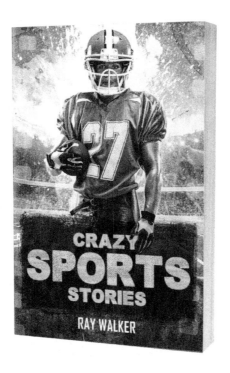

CONTENTS

INTRODUCTION

Students John Baynton and John Brodie were instrumental in forming St. Luke's FC and then seeing the church team develop into one of England's most famous and historic soccer clubs, Wolverhampton Wanderers.

The youngsters helped put the original squad together back in 1877, and the outfit is still going strong well over a century later in 2021.

Although Wolverhampton has experienced all four divisions of the professional English Football League, the side has spent most of its time competing in the top-tier.

Known by the nickname "Wolves," the club has captured several league titles throughout the years, as well as major trophies such as the FA and League Cups. The road has sometimes been a rocky one, though, with the team also having to endure relegation to the lower divisions on several occasions.

Wolves fans have plenty to be proud of due to the success of this relatively small club because they've always been able to hold their own against the big boys of English soccer, such as Manchester United, Liverpool, Chelsea, and Tottenham Hotspur.

The team has always entertained its fans from the day it was born with a much appreciated never-say-die attitude.

Wolves supporters have had the fortune of witnessing some of the world's top players and managers work their magic for almost 150 years now. They'll never forget the likes of characters such as John Brodie, Steve Bull, Johnny Hancocks, Peter Broadbent, Derek Dougan, Ally Robertson, Phil Parkes, Paul Ince, Andy Mutch, Rui Patrício, Sylvan Ebanks-Blake, Bakary Sako, Kenny Miller, Benik Afobe, Derek Parkin, Stan Cullis, Henri Camara, Billy Wright, Ron Flowers, Bert Williams, John Burridge, and Paul Bradshaw.

This trivia and fact book has been assembled to celebrate the Wanderers' wonderful history and achievements by re-living the club's history from the day it began in 1877 until 2021. You'll meet the side's most beloved players and managers and learn how each of them influenced the club in his own special way.

Wolverhampton's unique story is told here in lighthearted quiz form in 12 chapters, each representing a different topic. Each section features 20 brain-teasing quiz questions along with 10 educational "Did You Know?" facts. The questions are provided in multiple-choice and true-false formats, and the answers are revealed on a separate page.

This is the perfect instrument for challenging yourself on the astounding history of the Wolverhampton Wanderers and to challenge other Wolves and soccer supporters to quiz showdowns.

We hope the book will help refresh your knowledge of your favorite team and assist you in becoming the leader of the Wolves trivia pack!

CHAPTER 1:

ORIGINS & HISTORY

QUIZ TIME!

1. What year was the club founded?

   a. 1890

   b. 1883

   c. 1877

   d. 1871

2. The team originally played in the Southern League.

   a. True

   b. False

3. What is the team's nickname?

   a. Wolves

   b. The Dogs

   c. The Wanderers

   d. The Hounds

4. Which was NOT one of the club's early home grounds?

   a. James Harper's Field

   b. Dudley Road

c. Wolverhampton Common

d. Red House Park

5. Which club did the side play its first game against?

   a. Preston North End

   b. Everton Reserves

   c. Bristol Rovers FC

   d. Stafford Road Reserves

6. What was the club's original name?

   a. St. John's FC

   b. AFC Wolves

   c. Wolverhampton Athletic Club

   d. St. Luke's FC

7. The club has played its home games at Molineux Stadium since 1889.

   a. True

   b. False

8. Which two pupils were key founders of the club?

   a. George Worrall and Andy Morgan

   b. John Baynton and John Brodie

   c. John Brodie and Andy Morgan

   d. George Worrall and John Baynton

9. How many times has Wolverhampton been relegated as of 2020?

   a. 11

   b. 4

c. 9

d. 7

10. When did the club first introduce its own badge design?

    a. 1980-81

    b. 1975-76

    c. 1970-71

    d. 1962-63

11. Which side did Wolves play in their first Football League match?

    a. Burnley FC

    b. West Bromwich Albion

    c. Aston Villa

    d. Accrington FC

12. Wolverhampton first played in the West Midland League.

    a. True

    b. False

13. What was the team's original kit color?

    a. Grey and white stripes

    b. Sky blue

    c. Red and white stripes

    d. Orange

14. Who scored the squad's first goal in the Football League?

    a. David Wykes

    b. Joe Cooper

    c. Thomas Hunter

    d. Gershom Cox

15. Which was the first club Wolverhampton faced in the Premier League?

    a. Charlton Athletic FC
    b. Blackburn Rovers
    c. Manchester City FC
    d. Leicester City FC

16. Wolverhampton was a founding member of the Football League.

    a. True
    b. False

17. How many games did the team win in its first Football League campaign?

    a. 5
    b. 9
    c. 12
    d. 16

18. Which player scored the club's first Premier League goal?

    a. John O'Shea
    b. Colin Cameron
    c. Steffen Iversen
    d. Alex Rae

19. Which season did Wolverhampton first join the Premier League?

    a. 1992-93
    b. 1996-97

c. 2001-02

d. 2003-04

20. The club was first relegated after the 1905-06 season.

a. True

b. False

QUIZ ANSWERS

1. C – 1877

2. B – False

3. A – Wolves

4. C – Wolverhampton Common

5. D – Stafford Road Reserves

6. D – St. Luke's FC

7. A – True

8. B – John Baynton and John Brodie

9. A – 11

10. C – 1970-71

11. C – Aston Villa

12. B – False

13. C – Red and white stripes

14. D – Gershom Cox

15. B – Blackburn Rovers

16. A – True

17. C – 12

18. C – Steffen Iversen

19. D – 2003-04

20. A – True

DID YOU KNOW?

1. Wolverhampton Wanderers Football Club currently plays in the top-tier English Premier League and is based in the city of Wolverhampton in the West Midlands of England. The club, which is owned by the Chinese company Fosun International, is commonly known by its nickname of "Wolves." Its home games are played at Molineux Stadium.

2. The club was originally formed in 1877 as St. Luke's FC. The 2020-21 campaign was the club's 66th season in the top-tier of the English Football League and the seventh in the Premier League since it began in 1992-93.

3. Pupils John Baynton and John Brodie have been credited with founding the club after St. Luke's Church school students were given a soccer ball by their headmaster Harry Barcroft. The squad played its first game on January 13, 1877, against a reserve team from Stafford Road. Two years later, the club merged with a local soccer and cricket club named the Blakenhall Wanderers and formed Wolverhampton Wanderers in August 1879.

4. The team originally played at Goldthorn Hill, James Harper's Field, and Red House Park in 1879. The side moved in 1881 to a venue on Dudley Road, across from Fighting Cocks Inn. The team's first piece of silverware was the Wrekin Cup in 1884.

5. In 1888-89, the professional club was elected as one of 12

founding members of the English Football League and played its first match against Aston Villa on September 8, 1888. They finished their inaugural season in third place in the First Division and also reached the FA Cup final, losing 3-0 to league champions Preston North End. Wolves would win their first FA Cup in 1893 and were first relegated to the second tier in 1906.

6. The team moved to Molineux Stadium in 1889 and continues to play its home games there in 2020-21. The venue's current official capacity is 32,050. In 1923, Wolverhampton was relegated to the third-tier Third Division North. The club won the division the next season to return to the second tier, and in 1932-33, they finally earned promotion back to the top-flight First Division. The team won the First Division title for the first time in 1953-54.

7. The club went into receivership in 1982 and nearly folded due to financial difficulty resulting from expensive renovations to Molineux Stadium in 1979. The Wanderers were saved from liquidation when the club was purchased by a company named Allied Properties. However, after being promoted back to the top-flight, the side was relegated after three straight seasons and wound up in the fourth-tier Fourth Division.

8. In August 1986, the club was in receivership again and bailed out when Wolverhampton Council bought Molineux Stadium and the surrounding land, while Gallagher Estates

and the Asda Superstore chain paid off the outstanding debt. Both the club and Molineux Stadium were then purchased by lifelong fan Sir Jack Hayward in 1990.

9. Steve Morgan bought the club from Sir Jack Hayward in 2007 and sold it to Chinese investment group Fosun International in 2016 when it bought the club's parent company W.W. (1990) Limited and Morgan's Bridgemere Group. Wolves went on to win the second-tier Championship League in 2017-18 to return to the Premier League following a six-year absence.

10. Wolverhampton Wanderers Women's Football Club (WFC) was originally founded in 1975 as Heathfield Rovers and officially became associated with the men's club in 2008. The side, commonly referred to as Wolves' Women, played in the fourth tier of women's soccer in 2020-21 in the FA Women's National League Division One Midlands. The squad plays its home games at CKW Stadium in the Castlecroft area of the city and is known by the nicknames "Wolves," "She-Wolves," and "Wolfettes."

CHAPTER 2:

THE CAPTAIN CLASS

QUIZ TIME!

1. Who captained Wolves to their first FA Cup final?

    a. Charlie Mason

    b. Arthur Lowder

    c. David Wykes

    d. John Brodie

2. Wolverhampton has named 87 different players as full-time skippers as of 2020.

    a. True

    b. False

3. Conor Coady captained the Under-21 squad of which club before he joined Wolves?

    a. Liverpool FC

    b. Manchester United

    c. Blackburn Rovers

    d. West Bromwich Albion

4. Who did Billy Wright succeed as the team's captain?

a. Dennis Westcott

b. Johnny Haynes

c. Stan Cullis

d. Tom Galley

5. Keith Curle captained what club before joining Wolverhampton?

a. Huddersfield Town FC

b. Peterborough United

c. Mansfield Town FC

d. Manchester City FC

6. Who captained Wolves to promotion in the 2013-14 League One season?

a. Richard Stearman

b. Sam Ricketts

c. Danny Bath

d. Carl Ikeme

7. Norman Deeley wore the armband in the Wanderers' first UEFA tournament.

a. True

b. False

8. How many First Division titles did Billy Wright lead the side to?

a. 7

b. 5

c. 3

d. 2

9. Who captained Wolverhampton in its first Premier League campaign?

   a. Lee Naylor
   b. Paul Butler
   c. Henri Camara
   d. Denis Irwin

10. Which club did Karl Henry join after he was relieved of his Wolves captaincy?

    a. Queens Park Rangers
    b. Stoke City FC
    c. Swansea City FC
    d. Hull City FC

11. Who captained Wolves to the 1987-88 Football League Trophy?

    a. Andy Thompson
    b. Floyd Streete
    c. Steve Bull
    d. Ally Robertson

12. Billy Wright was skipper of the English men's national team a record 90 times.

    a. True
    b. False

13. Paul Butler left Wolverhampton to captain which outfit?

    a. Millwall FC
    b. Southampton FC

c. Leeds United

d. Bury FC

14. Conor Coady captained the English Under-17 squad to victory in what 2010 tournament?

    a. FIFA Youth Cup

    b. Toulon Tournament

    c. FIFA Under-17 World Cup

    d. UEFA European Under-17 Championship

15. Who did Roger Johnson replace as captain?

    a. Wayne Hennessey

    b. Karl Henry

    c. Kevin Doyle

    d. Stephen Ward

16. Mike Bailey lifted the League Cup in 1973-74.

    a. True

    b. False

17. Which club did Roger Johnson join Wolves from?

    a. Birmingham City FC

    b. Charlton Athletic

    c. Sheffield Wednesday

    d. Portsmouth FC

18. What player was named the club's vice-captain for the 2020-21 season?

    a. Daniel Podence

    b. Max Kilman

c. Willy Boly

d. Rúben Neves

19. Who captained Wolves to their first FA Cup final triumph in 1892-93?

    a. Stan Cullis

    b. Billy Slater

    c. Harry Allen

    d. Billy Wooldridge

20. Wolverhampton named a different captain for each month of the 2009-10 season.

    a. True

    b. False

QUIZ ANSWERS

1. D – John Brodie

2. B – False

3. A – Liverpool FC

4. C – Stan Cullis

5. D – Manchester City FC

6. B – Sam Ricketts

7. B – False

8. C – 3

9. B – Paul Butler

10. A – Queens Park Rangers

11. D – Ally Robertson

12. A – True

13. C – Leeds United

14. D – UEFA European Under-17 Championship

15. B – Karl Henry

16. A – True

17. A – Birmingham City FC

18. D – Rúben Neves

19. C – Harry Allen

20. B – False

DID YOU KNOW?

1. Hometown boy John Brodie was a key figure in the formative years of the club as he attended St. Luke's School in Blakenhall and was a founder of the team that became Wolverhampton Wanderers. He joined in 1877 and netted 12 goals in the side's first Football League season in 1888-89. Brodie also captained the squad in its first FA Cup final in 1888-89 when they lost 3-0 to Preston North End. He played three times for England and scored on his debut in March 1889 while wearing the captain's armband. Brodie retired from playing in 1891 due to a knee injury and became a referee. He returned to Wolves as a director of the club in June 1913.

2. Wolves Hall of Fame midfielder Ron Flowers kicked off his pro career with the side in 1952 and chipped in with 37 goals in 512 appearances. The England international wore the armband for his club and country and helped Wolves win three First Division titles, an FA Cup, two runner-up medals in the First Division and one in the Second Division. He also won, lost, and shared an FA Charity Shield. He scored six out of six penalty kicks with England and once scored in four straight games for his country. Flowers left Wolves in September 1967 for Northampton Town, where he later became player-manager. His younger brother, John, and uncle, George Flowers, both played pro soccer, as did his grandson Harry.

3. Arriving from Brentford in 1952, English international Bill Slater wore the armband for Great Britain at the 1952 Olympics and later wore it for Wolves. He won three First Division titles and two runner-up medals with the side as well as the 1959-60 FA Cup, in which he captained the side. He also won an FA Charity Shield and shared two others. The Wolves Hall-of-Famer was named the Football Writers' Association (FWA) Footballer of the Year for 1960. Slater scored 25 goals in 339 outings with the team before returning to Brentford in 1963.

4. Legendary English international midfielder/defender Billy Wright joined the club as a trainee in 1938 at the age of 14. He went on to become a member of the Wolverhampton and English Football Halls of Fame after scoring 16 times in 541 games. He became the first player to appear in 100 games for the English national side or any national team in the world, for that matter. Wright wore the armband for his country 90 times and was voted FWA Footballer of the Year for 1952. He won three First Division titles and runner-up medals and an FA Cup with Wolves as well as two shared FA Charity Shields. He played his entire career with the side, retiring in 1959 and later managing Arsenal.

5. Defender Conor Coady arrived from Huddersfield Town in 2015 and, in 2017-18, was named to the Championship League Team of the Season as the club won the title. He became full-time skipper in 2018-19 when the side returned to the Premier League. Coady played every minute of the

2019-20 Europa League campaign when the side reached the quarterfinals, and he was named to the Europa League Squad of the Season. He also once played every minute of 84 straight Premier League games. Coady has represented England from every level from under-16 to under-20 as well as the senior side. He captained the squad to victory at the 2010 European Under-17 Championship and skippered the side at the 2013 Under-20 World Cup. In August 2020, he became the first Wolves player to start for England since Steve Bull in 1990.

6. Known as one of Wolverhampton's greatest managers, English international midfielder Stan Cullis played his entire pro career with the club. He debuted in February 1935 and, within two years, was named captain. He helped the team finish as First Division runner-up in 1937-38 and 1938-39, as well as runner-up in the 1938-39 FA Cup. His career was interrupted by World War II, but he captained England and Wolves in several wartime games. Before kickoff in a 1938 game against West Germany in Berlin, Cullis refused to perform a Nazi salute and was temporarily dropped from the England team. He retired from playing in 1947 due to injury and was appointed assistant to manager Ted Vizard. Cullis took over the job between 1948 and 1964 and guided the side to several pieces of silverware.

7. Midfielder William Caddick left hometown Wellington Town for Wolves in 1920 and found himself relegated with his teammates to the Third Division North after the

1922-23 campaign. Caddick was then appointed captain to take over from Val Gregory and helped the side win the Third Division North the following season to return to the second tier. After approximately 150 appearances for the club, Caddick returned to Wellington Town in 1926-27.

8. When he arrived from Watford of the Southern League in May 1920, defender Valentine "Val" Gregory cost Wolves a £1,500 transfer fee, which was a record for Watford at the time. He helped the side reach the 1920-21 FA Cup final against Tottenham Hotspur and wore the skipper's armband during the game at Stamford Bridge in London. Gregory's side was relegated to the third tier following the 1922-23 campaign, and he then became a player-coach with a local amateur club while William Caddick took over as captain. Gregory hung up his boots in 1925 but remained at Molineux as a coach until 1938.

9. Former Manchester City captain Keith Curle joined Wolves in August 1996 for a reported £650,000 and spent four seasons at Molineux. The defender helped the team reach the second-tier playoffs in 1996-97, but they were beaten by Crystal Palace. Curle was then made captain, and he led the side to the FA Cup semifinals in 1997-98, but they were downed by eventual FA Cup and Premier League champions Arsenal. He joined Sheffield United in 2000 after appearing in more than 150 games with Wolves and became a football manager after hanging up his boots. In March 2021, Curle was named manager of Oldham Athletic.

10. Defender Paul Butler left Bury FC for Sunderland for £1 million in 1998 and won the second-tier First Division championship in his first season. He joined Wolves on loan in late 2000, and the move was made permanent in January 2001. Butler was appointed captain the next season and led the team to the playoffs, where they were beaten by Norwich City. The team won the 2002-03 playoffs 3-0 over Sheffield United to reach the Premier League for the first time but was relegated after just one season. Butler then joined another relegated club, Leeds United, in July 2004 and was made skipper shortly after signing.

CHAPTER 3:

AMAZING MANAGERS

QUIZ TIME!

1. Who was the club's first full-time secretary-manager?

    a. George Worrall

    b. Albert Hoskins

    c. George Jobey

    d. Major Frank Buckley

2. Between 1877 and 1922, Wolverhampton had seven different full-time managers.

    a. True

    b. False

3. In terms of silverware won, who is the most successful manager/secretary-manager in club history?

    a. Graham Turner

    b. Bill McGarry

    c. Stan Cullis

    d. Jack Addenbrooke

4. Mick McCarthy left which club to manage Wolverhampton?

    a. Manchester City FC

    b. Celtic FC

    c. Ipswich Town FC

    d. Sunderland AFC

5. How many full-time managers and secretary-managers has Wolves appointed as of April 2021?

    a. 45

    b. 31

    c. 24

    d. 19

6. Who led Wolves to their first FA Cup final?

    a. Albert Hoskins

    b. Jack Addenbrooke

    c. Ted Vizard

    d. George Worrall

7. Terry Connor did NOT win a single match in the 13 league games he managed the club.

    a. True

    b. False

8. How many Second Division titles did Major Frank Buckley win?

    a. 7

    b. 5

    c. 1

    d. 0

9. Who was the club's first manager born outside the British Isles?

   a. Walter Zenga
   b. Ståle Solbakken
   c. Sammy Chung
   d. Nuno Espírito Santo

10. Who was the Wanderers' first manager in the Premier League?

    a. Mick McCarthy
    b. Colin Lee
    c. Glenn Hoddle
    d. Dave Jones

11. How many trophies did Graham Turner win while leading Wolverhampton?

    a. 6
    b. 4
    c. 3
    d. 1

12. Ronnie Allen is the club's longest-serving manager/secretary-manager as of 2020.

    a. True
    b. False

13. Who did Nuno Espírito Santo replace as manager?

    a. Kenny Jackett
    b. Walter Zenga

c. Dean Saunders

d. Paul Lambert

14. Stan Cullis left Wolverhampton to manage what side?

    a. Preston North End

    b. Aston Villa

    c. Huddersfield Town FC

    d. Birmingham City FC

15. How many First Division titles did Stan Cullis win with Wolves?

    a. 9

    b. 6

    c. 5

    d. 3

16. Dean Saunders led the side to two league promotions.

    a. True

    b. False

17. Dave Jones joined Wolves from which team?

    a. Southampton FC

    b. Millwall FC

    c. Cardiff City FC

    d. West Bromwich Albion

18. Who succeeded Graham Turner as boss?

    a. Mark McGhee

    b. Colin Lee

    c. Sammy Chapman

    d. Graham Taylor

19. Who managed the club to promotion in the 2013-14 League One season?

   a. Walter Zenga
   b. Terry Connor
   c. Kenny Jackett
   d. Ståle Solbakken

20. Glenn Hoddle led Wolves to three First Division titles.

   a. True
   b. False

QUIZ ANSWERS

1. A – George Worrall

2. B – False

3. C – Stan Cullis

4. D – Sunderland AFC

5. B – 31

6. B – Jack Addenbrooke

7. A – True

8. C – 1

9. B – Ståle Solbakken

10. D – Dave Jones

11. C – 3

12. B – False

13. D – Paul Lambert

14. D – Birmingham City FC

15. D – 3

16. B – False

17. A – Southampton FC

18. D – Graham Taylor

19. C – Kenny Jackett

20. B – False

DID YOU KNOW?

1. The club's official website lists the following as its managers throughout history after the Premier League era began in 1992-93: Nuno Espírito Santo, May 2017 to Current day; Paul Lambert, October 2016 to May 2017; Walter Zenga, August 2016 to October 2016; Kenny Jackett, May 2013 to August 2016; Dean Saunders, January 2013 to May 2013; Ståle Solbakken, July 2012 to January 2013; Terry Connor, February 2012 to June 2012; Mick McCarthy, July 2006 to February 2012; Glenn Hoddle, December 2004 to July 2006; Dave Jones, January 2001 to November 2004; Colin Lee, November 1998 to December 2000; Mark McGhee, December 1995 to November 1998; Graham Taylor, March 1994 to November 1995; and Graham Turner, October 1986 to March 1994.

2. The club's managers before the Premier League era were: Sammy Chapman, November 1985 to August 1986; Bill McGarry, September 1985 to November 1985; Tommy Docherty, June 1984 to July 1985; Graham Hawkins, August 1982 to April 1984; Ian Greaves, February 1982 to August 1982; John Barnwell, November 1978 to January 1982; Sammy Chung, June 1976 to November 1978; Bill McGarry, November 1968 to May 1976; Ronnie Allen, September 1965 to November 1968; Andy Beattie, November 1964 to September 1965; Stan Cullis, June 1948 to September 1964; Ted Vizard, April 1944 to May 1948; Major Frank Buckley,

July 1927 to March 1944; Fred Scotchbrook, March 1926 to June 1927; Albert Hoskins, June 1924 to March 1926; George Jobey, June 1922 to May 1924; Jack Addenbrooke, August 1885 to June 1922; George Worrall, August 1877 to May 1885.

3. Wolverhampton's longest-serving manager was Jack Addenbrooke, from August 1885 to June 1922, for a total of 36 years and 10 months. The shortest spell belonged to Bill McGarry during his second stint in charge, from September 1985 to November 1985, just 61 days. The youngest manager when appointed was Jack Addenbrooke at the age of 20, and the oldest manager was Bill McGarry during his second stint at the age of 58.

4. All but three Wolves managers have hailed from the United Kingdom. Ståle Solbakken (2012-13) was born in Norway, Walter Zenga (2016) hailed from Italy, and current manager Nuno Espírito Santo (from 2017) was born in Portugal.

5. All but the UK club managers hailed from England. Ted Vizard and Dean Saunders were both born in Wales; Sammy Chapman was from Northern Ireland; Andy Beattie, Tommy Docherty, Mark McGhee, and Paul Lambert were born in Scotland; Kenny Jacket played internationally for Wales but was born in Watford, England; and Mick McCarthy played for the Republic of Ireland but was born in Barnsley, England.

6. From 1877 to 1922, the team was selected by a committee

that was run by a secretary with the same powers managers have today. Those who were considered secretary-managers were George Worrall from 1877 to 1885 and Jack Addenbrooke from 1885 to 1922. In June 1922, the club appointed George Jobey as the first full-time manager rather than secretary-manager.

7. When it comes to winning modern-era silverware with the club, the most successful manager has been former Wolves player Stan Cullis. He guided the side to three First Division championships, two FA Cups, and one FA Charity Shield during his time in charge, from June 1948 to September 1964. He was also the first manager to enter European competition with the club.

8. The only managers to win a major trophy with the team since Stan Cullis have been Bill McGarry and John Barnwell. McGarry won the League Cup in 1973-74, and Barnwell won the League Cup in 1979-80. McGarry also led the side to the UEFA Cup final in 1971-72 and to the Texaco Cup trophy in 1970-71.

9. Graham Turner was the club's boss between October 1986 and March 1994. He won three major trophies in the span of two seasons in the late 1980s. He guided the team to the Fourth Division title in 1987-88 and the Third Division crown in 1988-89. He also won the Football League Trophy in 1987-88.

10. Dave Jones, Mick McCarthy, and Nuno Espírito Santo have all managed the club during promotions to the

Premier League. Jones was in charge when the side captured the 2002-03 First Division playoffs. McCarthy was in charge when the team won the Championship League title in 2008-09, and Espírito Santo was at the helm in 2017-18 when the squad won the Championship League crown. Kenny Jackett also managed the team to a promotion in 2013-14 by winning the second-tier League One with a record points total of 103.

CHAPTER 4:

GOALTENDING GREATS

QUIZ TIME!

1. Who made more appearances in all competitions for the club?

   a. Mike Stowell
   b. Phil Parkes
   c. Bert Williams
   d. Tom Baddeley

2. Michael Oakes played in Wolverhampton's first Premier League game.

   a. True
   b. False

3. How many clean sheets did John Ruddy keep in the 2017-18 domestic league season?

   a. 24
   b. 21
   c. 16
   d. 12

4. Which keeper famously wore a Superman outfit under his kit during a game against Newcastle United?

a. Graham Stack

b. Jan Budtz

c. John Burridge

d. Carl Ikeme

5. Rui Patrício left what club to join Wolverhampton?

a. Athletic Bilbao

b. CF Valencia

c. Sporting CP

d. FC Porto

6. Who posted nine clean sheets in the 2016-17 Premier League?

a. Will Norris

b. Andy Lonergan

c. Harry Burgoyne

d. Carl Ikeme

7. Matt Murray appeared in all matches in the 2006-07 Championship League campaign.

a. True

b. False

8. How many appearances did Bert Williams make in all competitions for the squad?

a. 464

b. 420

c. 392

d. 371

9. Michael Oakes joined Wolverhampton from which outfit?

   a. Birmingham City FC

   b. Millwall FC

   c. Scarborough Athletic

   d. Aston Villa

10. How many clean sheets did Carl Ikeme post in the 2013-14 domestic league?

    a. 15

    b. 18

    c. 22

    d. 27

11. Which keeper was nicknamed "The Cat"?

    a. Andy Lonergan

    b. Aaron McCarey

    c. Bert Williams

    d. Emiliano Martínez

12. Rui Patrício played in every match in the 2019-20 Premier League season.

    a. True

    b. False

13. How many appearances did Mike Stowell make in all competitions with Wolves?

    a. 383

    b. 426

c. 448

d. 521

14. What was John Burridge's nickname?

    a. "Birdy"

    b. "Budgie"

    c. "JB"

    d. "Suitcase"

15. Who kept 13 clean sheets in the 2005-06 domestic league season?

    a. Matt Murray

    b. Stefan Postma

    c. Paul Jones

    d. Jan Budtz

16. Bert Williams was capped 24 times by the English men's national team.

    a. True

    b. False

17. Who appeared in 45 matches in the 2017-18 domestic league?

    a. John Ruddy

    b. Will Norris

    c. Rui Patrício

    d. Harry Burgoyne

18. How many appearances did Phil Parkes make for Wolves in all competitions?

a. 432

b. 416

c. 394

d. 382

19. How many clean sheets did Wayne Hennessey keep in the 2007-08 domestic league season?

    a. 8
    b. 14
    c. 19
    d. 21

20. Wolves had five different keepers make at least one appearance in the 2011-12 Premier League.

    a. True
    b. False

QUIZ ANSWERS

1. A – Mike Stowell

2. B – False

3. A – 24

4. C – John Burridge

5. C – Sporting CP

6. D – Carl Ikeme

7. B – False

8. B – 420

9. D – Aston Villa

10. C – 22

11. C – Bert Williams

12. A – True

13. C – 448

14. B – "Budgie"

15. B – Stefan Postma

16. A – True

17. A – John Ruddy

18. D – 382

19. C – 19

20. B – False

DID YOU KNOW?

1. Goalkeepers who have been voted by the fans with the Wolves Player of the Season award have been: Paul Bradshaw, 1980-81; Paul Bradshaw, 1981-82; John Burridge, 1982-83; Tim Flowers, 1984-85; Mike Stowell, 1990-91; Matt Murray, 2006-07; Wayne Hennessey, 2007-08; and Wayne Hennessey, 2011-12.

2. Tom Baddeley began his pro career in 1892 and joined Wolves in October 1896. He helped the team finish in third place in 1897-98 and then eighth and fourth the following two campaigns while posting 31 clean sheets in his first three years. He remained with the club until 1906-07 and played over 300 games as well as playing five times for England. Baddeley left in May 1907 for Bradford Park Avenue of the Southern League, where he was made club captain and helped them get elected to the Football League. His brother George played with Stoke City and West Bromwich Albion.

3. Before World War I broke out, Noel George played with Hednesford Town and joined Wolves in 1919 after the conflict ended. He was initially the backup to Teddy Peers and didn't make his senior debut until February 1921. George played in the FA Cup final soon after in just his 14th first-team outing and was edged 1-0 by Tottenham Hotspur. He became the first-choice keeper the next

season and helped the team win the Third Division North title in 1923-24. George posted 73 clean sheets in 242 appearances before retiring in 1928. Sadly, he passed away at the age of 32 in 1929 from gum disease.

4. Bert Williams played for Walsall before World War II and joined Wolves in 1945. The English international and Wolves Hall-of-Famer helped the club win the 1948-49 FA Cup and the 1953-54 First Division crown. Nicknamed "The Cat," he also played in Wolverhamton's famous floodlit friendly wins against Budapest Honvéd, Spartak Moscow, and Dynamo Moscow. Williams, who made 420 appearances for Wolves, ran a sports shop after hanging up his gloves and boots in 1957.

5. Another Wolves Hall of Fame member, Malcolm Finlayson of Scotland won the First Division title with the club in 1957-58 and 1958-59 as well as the 1959-60 FA Cup. He joined from Millwall in August 1956 for a reported £3,000 to act as backup for Bert Williams, but by 1957-58, he had become the first-choice keeper. He also played in the first few European tournaments for the team before retiring in May 1964 after making over 200 appearances. Finlayson spent a brief stint as Wolves vice-chairman in 1982.

6. Paul Bradshaw arrived from Blackburn Rovers for a Wolves record transfer fee of £150,000 in September 1977 after playing in the first-ever England under-21 international match. He wound up playing 243 times for the team and

helped it win the 1978-80 League Cup. He also played in two FA Cup semifinals and was named Player of the Year for 1980-81 and 1981-82. Bradshaw's side was relegated in 1982 but finished Second Division runner-up the next season to earn instant promotion. He then joined the Vancouver Whitecaps in Canada in 1984.

7. In a pro career that lasted 30 years and saw him play for well over two dozen clubs, John Burridge's seventh stop on his journey came at Wolverhampton. Nicknamed "Budgie," he arrived in July 1982 from Queens Park Rangers. He helped the just-relegated team gain promotion back to the top-flight as Second Division runner-up in 1982-83 when he was named the side's Player of the Season, only to be relegated again the following campaign. Burridge left Wolves in October 1984 for Sheffield United and continued playing the game until 1997. He was named goalkeeping consultant for the Kerala Blasters of India in 2019.

8. Michael Stowell spent 11 of his 20 pro years with Wolves between 1990 and 2001 and appeared in 448 games, a club high for a goalkeeper. He arrived at Wolverhampton on loan from Everton in 1989 and joined permanently a year later for a reported transfer fee of £275,000. He was named the club's Player of the Year for 1990-91 and didn't leave until a decade later when he joined Bristol City before retiring in May 2005. Stowell then became a coach at Leicester City and took over as caretaker manager several times.

9. Nicknamed "Lofty," Phil Parkes joined Wolves in 1962 from school and turned pro two years later. He debuted for the senior side in November 1966 and saved a penalty kick in a win over Preston North End. He was the number-one keeper for the next nine seasons and at one point played over 120 straight league outings. He won a UEFA Cup runner-up medal in 1971-72 after saving two penalties in the semifinals against Ferencváros. Parkes helped the team win the 1973-74 League Cup but missed the final with a broken ankle and helped it capture the Second Division title in 1976-77. After 382 appearances, he left Wolves to star in North America.

10. Welsh international Wayne Hennessey joined Wolverhampton's youth academy in 2003 and was loaned to Bristol City in July 2006 and Stockport County in January 2007. With Stockport, he set a Football League record of nine straight clean sheets and wins and went 857 minutes without conceding a goal. Wolves recalled him in April 2007, and he soon became the number-one keeper. He was named to the 2007-08 PFA Championship Team of the Year and was also the Wanderers' Player of the Season. Hennessey helped the team win the 2008-09 Championship League title and was voted the team's Player of the Season again for 2011-12. After several injuries, he was loaned to Yeovil Town in 2013 and joined Crystal Palace in January 2014 following 166 games with Wolves.

CHAPTER 5:

DARING DEFENDERS

QUIZ TIME!

1. Which player made more appearances in all competitions for Wolves?

   a. Billy Wright
   b. Derek Parkin
   c. John McAlle
   d. Geoff Palmer

2. Lee Naylor played in all 38 games in the 2003-04 Premier League season.

   a. True
   b. False

3. Who tallied five goals in the 2009-10 domestic league season?

   a. Ronald Zubar
   b. Joey Craddock
   c. Richard Stearman
   d. Christophe Berra

4. Derek Parkin joined Wolverhampton from which club?

   a. Portsmouth FC
   b. Stoke City FC
   c. Newcastle United
   d. Huddersfield Town FC

5. How many yellow cards was Richard Stearman shown in all competitions in 2014-15?

   a. 20
   b. 14
   c. 11
   d. 8

6. Which player appeared in 44 matches in the 2007-08 domestic league?

   a. Kevin Foley
   b. Neill Collins
   c. Darren Ward
   d. Michael Gray

7. Paul Butler was the only Wolves player shown a red card in all competitions in 2002-03.

   a. True
   b. False

8. How many appearances did John McAlle make in all competitions for Wolves?

   a. 581
   b. 565

c. 509

d. 490

9. Which player scored four goals in the 2004-05 Championship League season?

 a. Joleon Lescott

 b. Jody Craddock

 c. Lee Naylor

 d. Mikkel Bischof

10. Which player appeared in 57 matches in all competitions in 2019-20?

 a. Conor Coady

 b. Romain Saïss

 c. Jonny Otto

 d. Matty Doherty

11. Andy Thompson left Wolverhampton to play for which club?

 a. West Bromwich Albion

 b. Brighton & Hove Albion

 c. Chelsea FC

 d. Tranmere Rovers FC

12. Billy Wright played his entire professional career with Wolves.

 a. True

 b. False

13. How many goals did Stephen Ward tally in the 2012-13 domestic league campaign?

a. 7

b. 5

c. 2

d. 0

14. Which player tallied 14 assists in the 2017-18 Championship League season?

    a. Conor Coady

    b. Barry Douglas

    c. Matt Doherty

    d. Willy Boly

15. How many appearances did Billy Wright make in all competitions for the Wolves?

    a. 389

    b. 437

    c. 541

    d. 612

16. John McAlle was capped 13 times by the English men's national team while playing for Wolves.

    a. True

    b. False

17. How many appearances did Derek Parkin make in all competitions with Wolverhampton?

    a. 403

    b. 452

    c. 578

    d. 609

18. Which player appeared in all 46 matches in the 2013-14 League One season?

    a. Danny Batth
    b. Sam Ricketts
    c. Scott Golbourne
    d. Ethan Ebanks-Landell

19. Who played over 500 games with archrivals West Bromwich Albion before joining Wolves?

    a. George Elokobi
    b. Ally Robertson
    c. Michael Gray
    d. Stephen Ward

20. Billy Wright was capped 115 times by the English men's national team.

    a. True
    b. False

QUIZ ANSWERS

1. B – Derek Parkin

2. A – True

3. B – Joey Craddock

4. D – Huddersfield Town FC

5. C – 11

6. A – Kevin Foley

7. B – False

8. C – 509

9. A – Joleon Lescott

10. A – Conor Coady

11. D – Tranmere Rovers FC

12. A – True

13. C – 2

14. B – Barry Douglas

15. C – 541

16. B – False

17. D – 609

18. A – Danny Batth

19. B – Ally Robertson

20. B – False

DID YOU KNOW?

1. Defenders who have been voted by the club's fans as the Wolves Player of the Season are: Bob Hazell, 1977-78; George Berry, 1978-79; Alan Dodd, 1983-84; Floyd Streete, 1985-86; Steve Stoutt, 1986-87; Mark Venus, 1989-90; Andy Thompson, 1993-94; Keith Curle, 1997-98; Kevin Muscat, 1998-99; Ludovic Pollet, 1999-2000; Lee Naylor, 2000-01; Joleon Lescott, 2002-03; Joleon Lescott, 2004-05; Kevin Foley, 2008-09; Jody Craddock, 2009-10; Richard Stearman, 2014-15; and Matt Doherty, 2015-16.

2. After joining Wolves in 1900 from Lanesfield, Jackery Jones made his league debut in September 1901 and played 111 consecutive games before taking a break. He played in every game for five straight seasons from 1901-02 to 1906-07 and helped the side capture the 1907-08 FA Cup. Jones suffered a serious ankle injury in 1910 but didn't officially retire until 1913. He appeared in 334 games for the club, becoming the first player to reach the 300 mark, and chipped in with 16 goals. Jones later became an assistant trainer with the team and was inducted into its Hall of Fame.

3. The all-time appearance leader for the club is Derek Parkin with 609 between 1968 and 1982. He signed from Huddersfield Town for a fee of £80,000, which was then an English League record for a full-back. Known as "Mr.

Reliable," he would have played more games if he hadn't been sidelined for over half of the 1972-73 campaign with an illness. Parkin helped the side win the 1970-71 Texaco Cup, reach the 1971-72 UEFA Cup final, and win the 1973-74 and 1979-80 League Cups. Parkin also played 50 or more games in a season five times for the club. The Wolves Hall-of-Famer joined Stoke City in 1982 and retired a year later.

4. In October 1968, Wolves paid a reported £55,000 for Scottish international Frank Munro, who was a skilled midfielder converted into a center-back. He played 371 times for the club and helped the side reach the 1971-72 UEFA Cup final by scoring in both legs of the semifinal against Ferencváros. The Wolves Hall of Fame member won winners' medals in the 1970-71 Texaco Cup and the 1973-74 League Cup and played nine times for Scotland. After helping Wolves win the 1976-77 Second Division title, Munro joined Glasgow Celtic in December 1977.

5. Geoff Palmer arrived at Wolves in 1970 as an apprentice and played 496 times with the club. He helped the side win the 1973-74 League Cup, the 1976-77 Second Division, and the 1979-80 League Cup. He was one of just four Wolves players to win both of the team's League Cups and one of just two who appeared for the club in all four tiers of the English Football League. Palmer also helped earn promotion to the top-tier in 1982-83 by finishing as Second Division runner-up. He joined Burnley in November 1984 and rejoined Wolves in December 1985.

The team was relegated to the fourth tier for the first time in 1986, and after just one game in the Fourth Division in September 1986, Palmer hung up his boots to become a police officer.

6. Although Scotland's Ally Robertson played over 500 games and spent nearly two decades with archrivals West Bromwich Albion, he became a fan favorite and cult hero with Wolves. He arrived in 1986 and helped the team earn back-to-back promotions by winning the Fourth Division in 1987-88 and the Third Division in 1988-89. Robertson wore the captain's armband for West Brom and Wolves and hoisted the Football League Trophy at Wembley with the latter in 1987-88. After 130 appearances with Wolves, Robertson hung up his boots in 1990 after two decades in the game.

7. Andy "Thommo" Thompson was another defender who joined the club from West Bromwich Albion, as he signed alongside fellow Wolves Hall of Fame member Steve Bull in November 1986. He remained with the team until joining Tranmere Rovers in 1997 and contributed 45 goals in 451 appearances. Thompson was an expert penalty-taker and could also effectively play in other positions on the pitch. He helped the club win Fourth Division and Third Division titles as well as the 1987-88 Football League Trophy.

8. English international Joleon Lescott graduated from Wolverhampton's youth academy and debuted with the

senior side in 2000. He helped the side win the second-tier playoffs in 2002-03 and was named to the PFA First Division Team of the Year for 2001-02 and 2002-03 and was voted Wolves Player of the Season for 2002-03 and 2004-05. Unfortunately, he missed the entire 2003-04 campaign, and the team was relegated from the Premier League. Lescott was named to PFA Championship League Team of the Year for 2005-06. He was sold to Everton in August 2006 after more than 200 appearances.

9. Born in Kingston, Bob Hazell began his career at Wolves and played in the 1976 FA Youth Cup final loss to West Bromwich Albion. He played 20 First Division games in 1977-78 after making his debut in December 1977. He formed a fine central defensive partnership with John McAlle and was voted the team's Player of the Season for 1977-78. Hazell played just 13 times in 1978-79 before transferring to Queens Park Rangers for a reported £240,000 fee. He returned briefly on loan from Leicester City in 1985. After retiring, Hazell became a sports prevention manager, working to help rehabilitate young offenders through sport.

10. Following Bob Hazell as Wolves Player of the Season was fellow defender George Berry, who won the award for 1978-79. Berry was a German-born Welsh international who also joined the club as a youth. He turned pro on his 18th birthday and debuted for the side in May 1977 as the club won the 1976-77 Second Division title. Berry became a regular starter in the top-tier and helped the side

capture the 1979-80 League Cup. However, after the team was relegated, Berry joined Stoke City on a free transfer in July 1982 after 160 games with Wolves. He later became the senior commercial executive at the Professional Footballers' Association.

CHAPTER 6:

MAESTROS OF THE MIDFIELD

QUIZ TIME!

1. Which player made the most appearances in all competitions for Wolves?

   a. Derek Dougan
   b. Mike Bailey
   c. Kenny Hibbitt
   d. Ron Flowers

2. Paul Ince was shown 13 yellow cards in the 2003-04 Premier League season.

   a. True
   b. False

3. Who scored four goals in the 2019-20 domestic league season?

   a. Leander Dendoncker
   b. Rúben Neves
   c. João Moutinho
   d. Morgan Gibbs-White

4. Mike Bailey left what club to play for Wolves?

    a. Hereford United
    b. Doncaster Rovers FC
    c. Leeds United
    d. Charlton Athletic

5. How many goals did David Edwards score in the 2013-14 League One season?

    a. 12
    b. 9
    c. 6
    d. 4

6. How many appearances did Ron Flowers make in all competitions with Wolverhampton?

    a. 600
    b. 573
    c. 546
    d. 512

7. Colin Cameron made 28 appearances for the Scottish men's national team.

    a. True
    b. False

8. Which player appeared in 44 games in all competitions in 2013-14?

    a. Zeli Ismail
    b. David Davis

c. Kevin McDonald

d. Jack Price

9. Who was voted by the club's fans as the 2001-02 Player of the Season?

a. Mark Rankine

b. Alex Rae

c. Carl Robinson

d. Mark Kennedy

10. How many yellow cards was Rúben Neves shown in the 2017-18 domestic league season?

a. 3

b. 7

c. 8

d. 13

11. Who tallied 21 assists in all competitions in 2008-09?

a. David Edwards

b. Karl Henry

c. David Jones

d. Michael Kightly

12. Ron Flowers was capped 49 times by the English men's national team.

a. True

b. False

13. How many appearances did Kenny Hibbitt make in all competitions for Wolverhampton?

a. 466

b. 530

c. 574

d. 592

14. Willie Carr joined Wolverhampton from which side?

    a. Chelsea FC

    b. Sunderland AFC

    c. Millwall FC

    d. Coventry City FC

15. Who netted five goals in the 2003-04 Premier League season?

    a. Alex Rae

    b. Colin Cameron

    c. Shaun Newton

    d. Paul Ince

16. Karl Henry was shown two red cards in all competitions in 2010-11.

    a. True

    b. False

17. Who played in 44 games in the 2016-17 domestic league season?

    a. George Saville

    b. Jack Price

    c. David Edwards

    d. Ben Marshall

18. How many career games did Mike Bailey play for Wolverhampton?

    a. 415
    b. 436
    c. 547
    d. 565

19. Which player scored three goals in the 2017-18 Championship League campaign?

    a. Alfred N'Diaye
    b. Jack Price
    c. Connor Ronan
    d. Ben Stevenson

20. Kevin McDonald recorded 11 assists in the 2014-15 domestic league season.

    a. True
    b. False

QUIZ ANSWERS

1. C – Kenny Hibbitt

2. A – True

3. A – Leander Dendoncker

4. D – Charlton Athletic

5. B – 9

6. D – 512

7. A – True

8. C – Kevin McDonald

9. B – Alex Rae

10. C – 8

11. D – Michael Kightly

12. A – True

13. C – 574

14. D – Coventry City FC

15. A – Alex Rae

16. B – False

17. C – David Edwards

18. B – 436

19. A – Alfred N'Diaye

20. A – True

DID YOU KNOW?

1. Midfielders who have been voted by the team's fans with the Wolves Player of the Season award are: Steve Daley, 1976-77; Willie Carr, 1979-80; Tom Bennett, 1991-92; Paul Cook, 1992-93; Mark Rankine, 1994-95; Alex Rae, 2001-02; Matt Jarvis, 2010-11; Kevin McDonald, 2013-14; Hélder Costa, 2016-17; Rúben Neves, 2017-18.

2. Known for his leadership, Mike Bailey led the team back to the top-flight as captain in 1966-67 by finishing as Second Division runner-up, and they also went to the 1971-72 UEFA Cup final. He was on the side that won the League Cup in 1973-74 and the Second Division in 1976-77. Bailey arrived at Molineux from Charlton Athletic in March 1966 and left in 1977 when he went to play in America. He scored 25 times in 436 outings for Wolves, was elected to the club's Hall of Fame, and became a football manager after hanging up his boots.

3. Steve Daley began his career as a Wolves apprentice and debuted for the senior side in 1971 at the age of 18. He helped the side reach the 1971-72 UEFA Cup final and win the 1973-74 League Cup. He tallied 13 goals in 1976-77 and was voted the squad's Player of the Season. This led to being called up for six games with the England B team, where he scored twice. Daley was transferred to Manchester City in September 1979 for the odd price of £1,437,500, an English record at the time. Daley, who

played over 200 games with Wolves, later played indoor and outdoor soccer in America.

4. Wolves Player of the Season for 1979-80 was Scottish international Willie Carr. He had played nearly 300 games with Coventry City by the time he arrived at Molineux in March 1975 for a reported £80,000 fee, and he wound up in that club's Hall of Fame. Carr was just as reliable with Wolves, as he made 289 appearances and scored 26 goals before joining Millwall in 1982. He helped the team win the 1976-77 Second Division and the 1979-80 League Cup.

5. Mark Rankine's pro career lasted 19 years and more than 700 club games between 1987 and 2006. He spent four of those years at Molineux after arriving from Doncaster Rovers in January 1992 for a reported transfer fee of £70,000. Rankine was voted the club's Player of the Season for 1994-95 and appeared in nearly 170 games. He was sold to Preston North End for a reported £100,000 in September 1996. Rankine became a player agent later in life. He is the uncle of pro soccer players Michael Rankine, Danny Rose, and Mitch Rose.

6. Paul Cook was another former Wolves midfielder who enjoyed a long pro career in the game as he spent 23 years on the pitch and then became a manager. In fact, he just took over as boss at Ipswich Town on March 2, 2021. He kicked off his career in 1983 with Norwich City and went to Wolverhampton for a reported £250,000 in 1989. He was a favorite with the fans and his teammates and was voted Player of the Season for 1992-93. After 214 games

and 21 goals with the club, he joined Coventry City in 1994 for a reported £600,000.

7. Welsh international David Edwards arrived in January 2008 from Luton Town and scored in his debut five days later. He helped the side earn promotion to the Premier League by winning the 2008-09 Championship League title but was sidelined with an ankle injury for four months during his first campaign in the top-flight. He dealt with injuries over the next few seasons, and the team was relegated after both the 2011-12 and 2012-13 campaigns. Edwards then helped the squad win the third-tier League One title in 2013-14 by chipping in with nine league goals. He added 10 goals in the 2016-17 campaign and scored 44 total goals in 307 outings before joining Reading.

8. In August 2006, Karl Henry joined his hometown Wolverhampton team from Stoke City and spent much of his first season filling in as a defender. He wore the captain's armband for the first time just a few months after his debut and then suffered a season-ending injury. He returned to midfield in 2007-08 and wore the armband regularly the following year when skipper Jody Craddock was injured. He helped the side win the 2008-09 Championship League and became the full-time captain in the 2009-10 Premier League season. He was replaced as skipper in 2011-12 by Roger Johnson, and the team suffered two straight relegations. After 272 appearances in seven seasons, Henry joined Queens Park Rangers in July 2013.

9. English international Paul Ince had won several team and individual awards playing with West Ham United, Manchester United, Inter Milan, and Liverpool before joining Wolves from Middlesbrough in 2002. He helped the side right away, as Wolves earned promotion to the Premier League as Division One playoff winners in his first season. They were relegated the next year, but Ince remained with the club. He had planned on retiring following the 2004-05 campaign but decided to keep playing when Glenn Hoddle was appointed manager. Ince was hoping to take over as boss when Hoddle resigned in July 2006, but the job was given to Mick McCarthy, who decided not to offer Ince a new contract. After 131 games, Ince joined Swindon Town briefly in 2006 and soon became a manager. His son Tom played pro soccer as did his cousins, Rohan and Clayton Ince.

10. After making his debut with Gillingham as a 17-year-old in 2003, Matt Jarvis joined Wolverhampton in June 2007. He soon became a first-choice player, but the team missed making the playoffs due to an inferior goal difference. The team then won the 2008-09 Championship League to reach the Premier League and remained in the top-flight until being relegated following the 2011-12 campaign. Jarvis was voted the fans' and the players' Player of the Season awards for 2010-11. After requesting a transfer in August 2012, he was sold to West Ham United after scoring 21 goals in 175 matches.

CHAPTER 7:

SENSATIONAL STRIKERS & FORWARDS

QUIZ TIME!

1. Who appeared in the most contests with the club?

   a. Peter Broadbent

   b. Steve Bull

   c. John Richards

   d. Jimmy Mullen

2. Andy Keogh was shown seven yellow cards in the 2007-08 domestic league season.

   a. True

   b. False

3. Who scored 16 goals in all competitions in 2019-20?

   a. Patrick Cutrone

   b. Pedro Neto

   c. Adama Traoré

   d. Diogo Jota

4. Which player appeared in 30 league games in the 2003-04 campaign?

a. Kenny Miller

b. Henri Camara

c. Carl Cort

d. Ionel Ganea

5. How many goals did Matt Jarvis score in the 2009-10 domestic league season?

a. 11

b. 8

c. 3

d. 1

6. Peter Broadbent joined Wolves from which side?

a. Brentford FC

b. Aston Villa

c. Dover FC

d. West Ham United

7. Steve Bull was capped 13 times by the English men's national team.

a. True

b. False

8. Who made 40 appearances in the 2013-14 League One season?

a. Michael Jacobs

b. Leigh Griffiths

c. James Henry

d. Bakary Sako

9. How many goals did Hélder Costa score in the 2016-17 domestic league?

    a. 14
    b. 10
    c. 7
    d. 6

10. Which player tallied eight assists in the 2011-12 Premier League?

    a. Sam Vokes
    b. Adam Hammill
    c. Steven Fletcher
    d. Kevin Doyle

11. How many appearances did Steve Bull make in all competitions for Wolverhampton?

    a. 475
    b. 497
    c. 522
    d. 561

12. Raúl Jiménez played in all 38 matches in the 2018-19 Premier League season.

    a. True
    b. False

13. How many appearances did John Richards make for Wolves in all competitions?

    a. 520
    b. 514

c. 485

d. 432

14. How many goals did James Henry score in the 2015-16 domestic league?

    a. 4

    b. 7

    c. 8

    d. 12

15. Which team did Dave Wagstaffe leave to join Wolverhampton?

    a. Fulham FC

    b. Southampton FC

    c. Manchester City FC

    d. Blackburn Rovers

16. Jimmy Mullen played his entire professional career with Wolves.

    a. True

    b. False

17. Which player appeared in 35 games in all competitions in 2006-07?

    a. Jay Bothroyd

    b. Jemal Johnson

    c. Michael McIndoe

    d. Craig Davies

18. How many goals did Nouha Dicko score in all competitions in 2013-14?

a. 17

b. 13

c. 10

d. 8

19. How many appearances did Peter Broadbent make in all competitions for Wolverhampton?

a. 560

b. 523

c. 497

d. 468

20. Johnny Hancocks scored nine goals in five matches for the English men's national team.

a. True

b. False

QUIZ ANSWERS

1. B – Steve Bull

2. B – False

3. D – Diogo Jota

4. B – Henri Camara

5. C – 3

6. A – Brentford FC

7. A – True

8. D – Bakary Sako

9. B – 10

10. D – Kevin Doyle

11. D – 561

12. A – True

13. C – 485

14. B – 7

15. C – Manchester City FC

16. A – True

17. A – Jay Bothroyd

18. B – 13

19. C – 497

20. B – False

DID YOU KNOW?

1. Forwards who have been voted by Wolves fans to receive the Player of the Season award are: Steve Bull, 1987-88; Andy Mutch, 1988-89; Steve Bull, 1995-96; Steve Bull, 1996-97; Henri Camara, 2003-04; Kenny Miller, 2005-06; Bakary Sako, 2012-13; Raúl Jiménez, 2018-19; and Raúl Jiménez, 2019-20.

2. Wolverhampton paid £400 to Crewe Alexandra for winger Billy Harrison in 1907. He immediately helped the side reach the 1907-08 FA Cup final in his first season and scored in their 3-1 upset win over Newcastle United. His wife gave birth to triplets on the morning of the final. Harrison played for the club before and after World War I, scoring 49 goals in 345 appearances. He joined Manchester United in October 1920 and retired at the age of 38 in 1924. Harrison was inducted into the Wolves Hall of Fame in 2009.

3. Winger Norman Deeley played with Wolves from 1951 to 1962 and scored twice in the team's 1959-60 FA Cup final victory to win the Man of the Match award. He also helped the side win three First Division titles and an FA Charity Shield, and they shared two other Charity Shields. He was capped twice by England. He notched 23 goals in 1957-58 and 17 the following season. When Deeley played for the England Schoolboys side in 1947, he

was just 4 feet 4 inches tall, making him the shortest player ever for the team at the time. He joined Leyton Orient in February 1962 and hung up his boots in 1964. Deeley's son Andy played for the New Zealand men's national soccer team.

4. At just 5 feet 4 inches tall, winger Johnny Hancocks began his pro career just before World War II broke out and joined Wolves from Walsall in 1946. He notched 10 goals in his first season and shared the team lead with Jesse Pye in his second campaign with 16 goals. This led to a call-up from the English national team, and he scored twice on his debut against Switzerland in 1948. However, he played just twice more for his country. Hancocks helped Wolves win the 1948-49 FA Cup and 1953-54 First Division title, as well as share the FA Charity Shield in 1949 and 1954. The Wolves Hall-of-Famer led the team in scoring in 1954-55 and 1955-56 and notched 168 goals for Wolves in 378 appearances before joining non-league Wellington Town as player-manager in 1957.

5. Winger Jimmy Mullen arrived at Wolverhampton in 1937 as an English schoolboy and turned pro on his 17th birthday two years later. He stayed with the club until hanging up his boots in May 1960 and netted 112 goals in 486 games, with World War II interrupting his career. Mullen helped the team win an FA Cup and three First Division titles, and shared two FA Charity Shields. The Wolves Hall of Fame member scored six goals in 12 games for England, played in two World Cups, and

became the team's first-ever substitute in a game against Belgium in May 1950.

6. Wolves Hall of Fame member Andy Mutch was playing for non-league Southport when the club signed him in February 1986. He scored seven goals in 15 games over the remainder of the season, but the side was relegated to the fourth-tier Fourth Division. Mutch was then partnered up front with Steve Bull, and the squad reached the playoffs. The pair combined for 53 league goals in 1987-88 to win the Fourth Division title and combined for 58 league goals the following campaign to hoist the Third Division crown. Mutch also won the Football League Trophy in 1987-88, was voted the team's Player of the Season in 1988-89, and scored 106 goals for the club before joining Swindon Town in 1993.

7. Striker Henri Camara, who played 99 times for Senegal, began his pro career in France and Switzerland before joining newly promoted Wolves in the Premier League from Sedan in 2003. He scored seven goals in 30 league games and was named the club's Player of the Season. However, the team was relegated to the second tier. Camara didn't want to play in the lower level and didn't show up for pre-season training. Bolton Wanderers then bid for Camara, but he was sent to Glasgow Celtic and then Southampton on loan in 2004-05. Southampton was relegated on the last day of the season, and Camara was sold to Wigan Athletic.

8. Scottish international Kenny Miller arrived at Molineux on loan from Glasgow Rangers in September 2001 and made the move permanent in December 2001 for a reported £3 million fee. In 2002-03, he notched 24 goals in all appearances to help the team win the second-tier playoffs. However, he managed just five goals in 2003-04, and Wolverhampton was relegated from the Premier League. Miller bounced back with 20 goals in 2004-05 and scored 12 in 2005-06 to be named the team's Player of the Season. Miller led the side in scoring in three seasons and totaled 63 goals in 191 games before joining Glasgow Celtic on a free transfer in 2006.

9. Another player who led Wolves in scoring for three seasons was Sylvan Ebanks-Blake, who topped the hit parade in 2007-08, 2008-09, and 2012-13 with 12, 25, and 15 goals, respectively. He arrived from Plymouth Argyle in January 2008 and totaled 23 goals that campaign to win the Championship League Golden Boot with 12 for Wolves and 11 for Plymouth. He helped the team win the Championship League title in 2008-09 and won the Golden Boot again as well as being named to the PFA Championship League Team of the Year, the league's Player of the Year, and scorer of the Football League Goal of the Year. He remained at Molineux until being released after the 2012-13 season when the team was relegated. Ebanks-Blake then joined Ipswich Town.

10. Forward/midfielder Bakary Sako was born in France but played senior international football with Mali. He arrived

from Saint-Étienne in 2012 and scored in his first Wolves outings. He posted 10 goals and 11 assists in his first campaign to be voted the team's Player of the Season, but the side was relegated to third-tier League One. Wolves reportedly rejected several offers from Nottingham Forest for Sako, and he stayed to help the team win the League One title while being named to the PFA League One Team of the Year. He was then named to the PFA Championship League Team of the Year for 2014-15 but joined Crystal Palace in August 2015. Sako shared the scoring lead for Wolves in 2013-14 and 2014-15 and tallied 38 goals in 124 games.

CHAPTER 8:

NOTABLE TRANSFERS & SIGNINGS

QUIZ TIME!

1. Which Wolves player has been the most expensive transfer signing as of April 2021?

    a. Fábio Silva

    b. Nélson Semedo

    c. Jonny Otto

    d. Raúl Jiménez

2. Wolverhampton did not make an official transfer signing in 2007-08.

    a. True

    b. False

3. Who was the most expensive transfer acquisition in 2010-11?

    a. Steven Mouyokolo

    b. Steven Fletcher

    c. Jelle Van Damme

    d. Stephen Hunt

4. Who was sold for Wolverhampton's highest transfer fee received?

   a. Hélder Costa
   b. Matt Doherty
   c. Steven Fletcher
   d. Diogo Jota

5. Which club was Nélson Semedo signed from?

   a. FC Barcelona
   b. Juventus
   c. Ajax
   d. FC Porto

6. How much did Wolves pay to acquire Nélson Semedo?

   a. £39 million
   b. £32 million
   c. £27 million
   d. £24 million

7. Wolverhampton signed Kevin Doyle from Burnley FC for a fee of £10 million.

   a. True
   b. False

8. Which club did Wolves transfer Diogo Jota to?

   a. Chelsea FC
   b. AS Saint-Étienne
   c. AC Milan
   d. Liverpool FC

9. How much did Wolverhampton sell Hélder Costa for?

   a. £12.50 million

   b. £15.93 million

   c. £24 million

   d. £33 million

10. Wolves sold Benik Afobe to what club in the 2018-19 season?

    a. Stoke City FC

    b. Arsenal FC

    c. Newcastle United

    d. Aston Villa

11. Who was the club's most expensive signing in 2013-14?

    a. Nouha Dicko

    b. Michael Jacobs

    c. Kevin McDonald

    d. Bradley Reid

12. Wolverhampton signed four players from Derby County FC in the 2013-14 season.

    a. True

    b. False

13. How much did Wolves acquire Raúl Jiménez for?

    a. £40.25 million

    b. £36 million

    c. £34.2 million

    d. £31 million

14. Who was Wolverhampton's most expensive departure in 2005-06?

    a. Henri Camara
    b. Joleon Lescott
    c. Shaun Newton
    d. Seol Ki-hyeon

15. What was the transfer fee Wolves received for selling Diogo Jota?

    a. £32 million
    b. £36 million
    c. £40.23 million
    d. £45 million

16. Peter Broadbent was just 17 years old when signed from Brentford in 1951.

    a. True
    b. False

17. How much did the club pay to acquire Fábio Silva?

    a. £45 million
    b. £36 million
    c. £31 million
    d. £28 million

18. Who was Wolverhampton's most expensive transfer signing in 2014-15?

    a. Conor Coady
    b. Joe Mason

c. George Saville

d. Benik Afobe

19. What was the transfer fee Wolverhampton received for selling Matt Doherty?

    a. £34.26 million

    b. £27 million

    c. £15.12 million

    d. £13 million

20. Wolves signed Raúl Jiménez from SL Benfica.

    a. True

    b. False

QUIZ ANSWERS

1. A – Fábio Silva

2. B – False

3. B – Steven Fletcher

4. D – Diogo Jota

5. A – FC Barcelona

6. C – £27 million

7. B – False

8. D – Liverpool FC

9. B – £15.93 million

10. A – Stoke City FC

11. C – Kevin McDonald

12. B – False

13. C – £34.2 million

14. A – Henri Camara

15. C – £40.23 million

16. A – True

17. B – £36 million

18. D – Benik Afobe

19. C – £15.12 million

20. A – True

DID YOU KNOW?

1. As of April 2021, the top five transfer fees paid by Wolves are: forward Fábio Silva from FC Porto for £36 million in 2020-21; forward Raúl Jiménez from SL Benfica for £34.2 million in 2019-20; defender Nélson Semedo from FC Barcelona for £27 million in 2020-21; defender Jonny Otto from Atlético Madrid for £18.9 million in 2018-19; winger Adama Traoré from Middlesbrough FC for £18 million in 2018-19.

2. As of April 2021, the top five transfer fees received by Wolves are: winger Diogo Jota to Liverpool FC for £40.23 million in 2020-21; winger Hélder Costa to Leeds United for £15.93 million in 2020-21; defender Matt Doherty to Tottenham Hotspur for £15.12 million in 2020-21; forward Steven Fletcher to Sunderland AFC for £13.68 million in 2012-13; forward Benik Afobe to Stoke City for £12.15 million in 2018-19.

3. English international and Wolves Hall of Fame member Peter Broadbent arrived in February 1951 from Brentford at the age of 17 and proceeded to score 145 goals in 497 games for the squad. His transfer fee was £10,000, which made him the most expensive teenager in the country at the time. He helped the side win three First Division championship medals, an FA Cup, and an FA Charity Shield. Broadbent led the team in scoring with 22 goals in

1958-59 and played in England's first-ever under-23 international in 1954. However, he played for the senior side just seven times. Broadbent remained with Wolves until joining Shrewsbury Town in 1965.

4. Fábio Silva has been Wolverhampton's costliest transfer signing so far after arriving from Porto in his homeland for £36 million in September 2020. With Porto, he became the youngest player in club history at 17 years and 22 days He was also the youngest Porto player to appear in European competition and the youngest to score a goal. Silva inked a five-year deal with Wolves and became the club's youngest Premier League scorer on December 20, 2020. The striker has played under-15 to under-19 football with Portugal and had played in 29 games with Wolves as of April 20, 2021, with three goals to his name.

5. The second-most expensive acquisition was Mexican international forward Raúl Jiménez from Benfica for £34.2 million. He originally joined in June 2018 on a season-long loan for a fee of £2.7 million. Jiménez was a hit with 13 league goals, and 17 overall, in 44 appearances and was voted the team's Player of the Season. Wolves paid his buyout fee in April 2019, and he followed up in 2019-20 with a club-record 17 Premier League goals and 27 in all competitions and was voted Player of the Season again. Jiménez fractured his skull in a game against Arsenal in November 2020, which sidelined him for the season with 48 goals scored in 110 games for the team.

6. Portuguese international forward Diogo Jota arrived at Molineux in July 2017 on a season-long loan from Atlético Madrid, and in July 2018, the deal was made permanent for a fee of £10.8 million. He notched a career-best 17 league goals in his first season to help the team win the Championship League and earn promotion to the Premier League. In January 2019, Jota became the second Portuguese player after Cristiano Ronaldo to score a Premier League hat-trick, and he netted 10 goals in 37 games. Jota added 16 goals in 2019-20 for a total of 44 in 131 games. He was then sold to Liverpool in September 2020 for a club-record £40.23 million and a very healthy profit.

7. In the summer of 2018, Wolves paid £16.2 million to Sporting Lisbon for goalkeeper Rui Patrício. He debuted with Sporting as an 18-year-old and appeared in over 450 games with the club, helping it win five trophies over 12 years. With plenty of club and international experience, he signed a four-year deal and chose to wear the number 11 shirt in honor of former Wolves keeper Carl Ikeme, who had retired due to leukemia treatment. Patrício posted nine clean sheets in his first season and 13 in his second. As of April 20, 2021, he had played 122 times for Wolves and 92 times for Portugal, making him that nation's most-capped keeper.

8. The first £1 million transfer fee paid by Wolves was for Scottish international striker Andy Gray from Aston Villa in September 1979. He tallied 46 goals in 62 appearances

with Dundee United to start his career and joined Villa as a 19-year-old in 1975 for £110,000. He shared the First Division Golden Boot in 1976-77 with Arsenal's Malcolm Macdonald at 29 goals each. Villa also won the League Cup, and Gray was named the PFA Young Player of the Year and became the youngest player to capture the PFA Players' Player of the Year award. Gray joined Wolves for an English record fee of £1.5 million and scored the winning goal in the 1979-80 League Cup final. The club was relegated in 1982 but promoted the following season, and Gray joined Everton in November 1983 for a reported £250,000 after scoring 38 goals in 133 games.

9. Striker Benik Afobe of the Democratic Republic of Condo was sold from Wolves to Stoke City in January 2019 for £12.15 million and to Bournemouth in January 2016 for £11.97 million. In between, Wolves bought him back from Bournemouth in the summer of 2018 for £10.26 million. Afobe was signed by Arsenal in 2010 but was loaned to several clubs before Wolves bought him in January 2015 for £2.34 million. After scoring 23 goals in 48 games, he was sold to Bournemouth a year later, and two years after that, he rejoined Wolves on loan. Afobe scored six goals in 16 appearances to help the team win the 2017-18 Championship League title, and the move became permanent. He was immediately loaned to Stoke as part of a permanent deal, which netted Wolves a quick £2 million profit.

10. Midfielder/forward Hélder Costa was born in Angola and

plays internationally for Portugal. He arrived in July 2016 on loan from Benfica and was signed for £13.50 million on a permanent transfer in January 2017, which was then a Wolves record. He tallied 12 goals in his first season and was voted the team's Player of the Season award and also won the Players' Player of the Year and Goal of the Season awards. He helped the team win the 2017-18 Championship League title but, in July 2019, was loaned to Leeds United and joined them outright a year later for £15.93 million.

CHAPTER 9:

ODDS & ENDS

QUIZ TIME!

1. Who scored Wolverhampton's fastest goal on record against Burnley FC in just 15 seconds?

    a. Jimmy Murray

    b. Kenny Hibbitt

    c. Andy Mutch

    d. John Richards

2. In 1887, Charlie Mason became the first Wolves player to be capped by the English men's national team.

    a. True

    b. False

3. Who won the 1951-52 FWA Footballer of the Year award?

    a. Bill Slater

    b. Jimmy Dunn

    c. Billy Wright

    d. Roy Pritchard

4. The Wanderers' biggest victory in any competition was 14-0 against which club?

   a. Crosswell's Brewery FC
   b. Crewe Alexandra FC
   c. Nottingham Forest FC
   d. Fulham FC

5. What is the most goals Wolverhampton has scored in a domestic league season as of 2019-20?

   a. 123
   b. 115
   c. 108
   d. 96

6. Who was the youngest player to make an appearance for the club at the age of 16 years and 43 days?

   a. Chem Campbell
   b. Harry Wood
   c. Morgan Gibbs-White
   d. Jimmy Mullen

7. Wolverhampton was the first club ever to be awarded and score a penalty kick in the English Football League.

   a. True
   b. False

8. What is the most wins the club has posted in a domestic league season as of 2019-20?

   a. 27
   b. 29

c. 31

d. 33

9. The Wanderers' biggest league victory was a 10-1 win against what outfit?

    a. Stoke City FC

    b. Leeds United

    c. Leicester City FC

    d. Chelsea FC

10. What is the most games Wolverhampton has won in a Premier League season as of 2019-20?

    a. 24

    b. 13

    c. 20

    d. 16

11. The Black Country Derby is the name of the rivalry between Wolves and which other club?

    a. Birmingham City FC

    b. West Bromwich Albion

    c. Aston Villa

    d. Stoke City FC

12. Wolverhampton's record for the longest unbeaten streak in domestic league competition is 34 games as of 2019-20.

    a. True

    b. False

13. How many contests did the side draw in the 2004-05 Championship League?

a. 10

b. 16

c. 21

d. 25

14. The Wanderers' biggest defeat in all competitions was 10-1 to which team in 1892?

a. Newton Heath

b. Tottenham Hotspur

c. Blackburn Rovers

d. Leicester City FC

15. Who was the oldest player to make an appearance for the club at the age of 41 years and 116 days?

a. Paul Ince

b. Marcus Hahnemann

c. Archie Goodall

d. Denis Irwin

16. Billy Hartill scored five goals in a single match on three separate occasions with Wolves.

a. True

b. False

17. How many games did the squad lose in the 1983-84 First Division season?

a. 27

b. 25

c. 22

d. 19

18. Wolverhampton's record home attendance of 61,315 was set against which side?

    a. Aston Villa
    b. Birmingham City FC
    c. Manchester United
    d. Liverpool FC

19. What is the most points Wolves has recorded in a domestic league season as of 2019-20?

    a. 94
    b. 99
    c. 103
    d. 107

20. Joe Butcher was Wolverhampton's first player to score five goals in a league match.

    a. True
    b. False

QUIZ ANSWERS

1. D – John Richards

2. A – True

3. C – Billy Wright

4. A – Crosswell's Brewery FC

5. B – 115

6. D – Jimmy Mullen

7. A – True

8. C – 31

9. C – Leicester City FC

10. D – 16

11. B – West Bromwich Albion

12. B – False

13. C – 21

14. A – Newton Heath

15. C – Archie Goodall

16. B – False

17. B – 25

18. D – Liverpool FC

19. C – 103

20. A – True

DID YOU KNOW?

1. Before current seating regulations were introduced, Molineux Stadium could hold more than 60,000 fans. The record attendance was 61,315 for a First Division match against Liverpool on February 11, 1939. The stadium's name comes from a local merchant named Benjamin Molineux who built Molineux House in 1744 and later converted it to the Molineux Hotel. O.E. McGregor bought the land in 1860 and converted it to a public multi-sports park named Molineux Grounds.

2. The Northampton Brewery bought Molineux Grounds in 1889 and rented the venue to Wolves. The site was renovated, and the first league match was played on September 7, 1889, a 2-0 win over Notts County in front of 4,000 fans. The club bought the venue in 1923 and developed it by adding bigger stands and terraces.

3. Wolves became one of the first British soccer clubs to install floodlights in their stadium in 1953. The first game played under the lights at Molineux resulted in a 3-1 victory over South Africa on September 30, 1953. With floodlights now in place, Wolves was able to host midweek friendlies against national teams from around the world. In 1957, taller floodlights were installed.

4. Molineux Stadium was renovated several times over the years, with a newer version officially opening on

December 7, 1993, with a friendly game against Hungarian club Honvéd. The record attendance for the stadium in its current configuration was 31,746 in a Premier League game against Liverpool on January 23, 2020.

5. Wolverhampton's traditional colors of gold shirts and black shorts relate to the city council's motto "out of darkness cometh light," as the colors represent light and darkness, respectively. However, the team's original colors were red and white, the colors of St. Luke's School. During the early years, the side wore a variety of shirt designs, such as stripes and diagonal halves until the 1930s. The traditional away colors were all white, but in recent decades, the club has worn other colors including blue, black, maroon, teal, and purple.

6. The team's earliest shirts typically featured a badge on special occasions, such as cup finals. The first badge worn was the Wolverhampton City Council coat of arms. The club later designed its own badge, which featured a leaping wolf. This was changed in the mid-1970s to three leaping wolves, and since 1979, it has featured just a lone wolf head. The badge was redesigned in 2002.

7. In May 2019, the club won a legal challenge by a man named Peter Davies, who claimed he created the wolf head design in the 1960s when he entered it in a school competition. Mr. Davies copyrighted the design and felt he was entitled to compensation. The court rejected the copyright infringement claim, and Davies reportedly

faced costs and legal fees amounting to approximately £450,000.

8. Wolves became the first club to score at least 100 goals in four straight English League campaigns, from 1957-58 to 1960-61. They were also the first outfit to win the league championship in all four tiers of the professional English Football League and the first to win all of the main domestic cup competitions: the FA Cup, League Cup, and Football League Trophy.

9. In 2005, the club became the first in the English Football League to tally 7,000 league goals. The team also shares the record for the biggest away victory in the top flight by beating Cardiff City 9-1 on November 3, 1955. In addition, the first player to make 100 appearances for the English men's national team was former Wolves skipper Billy Wright.

10. The signature song for Wolves home fans in the 1950s was "The Happy Wanderer," which was a UK hit in 1954 when the club won the top-tier crown for the first time. Since then, fans have modified a 1967 song called "Hi Ho Silver Lining" that was made popular by rock guitarist Jeff Beck, with the chorus changed to "Hi Ho Wolverhampton."

CHAPTER 10:

DOMESTIC COMPETITION

QUIZ TIME!

1. Which club did Wolves face in their first FA Cup final?

    a. Aston Villa

    b. Newton Heath

    c. Preston North End

    d. Burnley FC

2. Wolverhampton won the First Division in three consecutive seasons between 1957-58 and 1958-59.

    a. True

    b. False

3. How many times has Wolves won the FA Charity/ Community Shield outright as of 2020?

    a. 1

    b. 3

    c. 4

    d. 6

4. What was the first major domestic trophy Wolves won?

a. FA Charity Shield

b. First Division Title

c. Second Division Title

d. FA Cup

5. Which season did the side win the Football League Trophy?

a. 1979-80

b. 1983-84

c. 1987-88

d. 2008-09

6. Who did Wolverhampton defeat to win their first FA Cup?

a. Blackburn Rovers

b. Sunderland AFC

c. Everton FC

d. West Bromwich Albion

7. Wolves has not won the Premier League as of 2020-21.

a. True

b. False

8. How many times has Wolverhampton reached the FA Cup final as of 2021?

a. 10

b. 8

c. 7

d. 5

9. Who scored the winning goal in the 1892-93 FA Cup final?

    a. Harry Allen
    b. Arthur Griffin
    c. David Wykes
    d. Harry Wood

10. Wolves defeated which club to win the 1987-88 Football League Trophy final?

    a. Halifax Town AFC
    b. Notts County FC
    c. Torquay United
    d. Burnley FC

11. How many times has the team won the League Cup as of 2021?

    a. 1
    b. 2
    c. 4
    d. 6

12. Wolverhampton won the Birmingham Senior Cup seven times.

    a. True
    b. False

13. Who scored the winning goal in the 1987-88 Football League Trophy final?

    a. Micky Holmes
    b. Robbie Dennison

c. Steve Bull

d. Andy Mutch

14. Which outfit did Wolves face in the 1949 FA Charity Shield?

a. Portsmouth FC

b. Arsenal FC

c. Manchester United

d. Newcastle United

15. What was the first season the side played in the League Cup final?

a. 1990-91

b. 1979-80

c. 1973-74

d. 1959-60

16. Wolves hoisted the 1941-42 Football League War Cup.

a. True

b. False

17. Which squad did Wolverhampton play in their first League Cup final?

a. Tottenham Hotspur

b. Norwich City FC

c. Leeds United

d. Manchester City FC

18. Who netted the winner in the 1948-49 FA Cup final?

a. Sammy Smyth

b. Jimmy Dunn

c. Johnny Hancocks

d. Jesse Pye

19. How many times did Wolves finish as runner-up in the top-tier First Division?

a. 2

b. 3

c. 5

d. 7

20. Wolves won two fourth-tier Fourth Division championships.

a. True

b. False

QUIZ ANSWERS

1. C – Preston North End

2. B – False

3. A – 1

4. D – FA Cup

5. C – 1987-88

6. C – Everton FC

7. A – True

8. B – 8

9. A – Harry Allen

10. D – Burnley FC

11. B – 2

12. A – True

13. D – Andy Mutch

14. A – Portsmouth FC

15. C – 1973-74

16. A – True

17. D – Manchester City FC

18. D – Jesse Pye

19. C – 5

20. B – False

DID YOU KNOW?

1. Wolverhampton's longest and fiercest rivalry is with West Bromwich Albion, which is based just 11 miles away. Games between the two teams are known as the Black Country Derby. The clubs first met each other competitively in the FA Cup tournament in 1886. Both clubs were founding members of the English Football League in 1888-89.

2. The club also has local rivalries with the two teams based in Birmingham, Aston Villa and Birmingham City. The closest geographical club to Wolves is actually Walsall. However, there isn't much of a rivalry between the sides because they rarely compete in the same Football League division. There's also a lesser rivalry, known as the Staffordshire Derby, between Wolves and Stoke City.

3. As of 2020-21, Wolves has been crowned the top-tier First Division Champions three times in club history but have never won the Premier League since its inception in 1992-93. The club has also finished as First Division runner-up five times. The side has won the second-tier Second Division/Championship League title four times and finished runner-up twice while winning the playoffs once. They have also won a third-tier Third Division/League One title three times and a fourth-tier Fourth Division championship once.

4. As far as domestic cups go, Wolves has hoisted the FA Cup on four occasions and finished as runner-up four times as well. The side has won the League Cup twice and the Football League Trophy once. They have also captured the FA Charity/Community Shield once, shared it three times, and lost it once.

5. The team's First Division titles were won in 1953-54, 1957-58, and 1958-59. They finished second in 1937-38, 1938-39, 1949-50, 1954-55, and 1959-60. The side won the Second Division title in 1931-32 and 1976-77 and captured the Championship League in 2008-09 and 2017-18. They finished runner-up in the Second Division in 1966-67 and 1982-83 and won the second-tier First Division playoffs in 2003.

6. Wolves took home the Third Division North title in 1923-24 and the Third Division crown in 1988-89. The side won the League One championship in 2013-14 and captured the Fourth Division title in 1987-88.

7. The Wanderers were crowned FA Cup champions in 1892-93, 1907-08, 1948-49, and 1959-60 and finished as runners-up in 1888-89, 1895-96, 1920-21, and 1938-39. They hoisted the League Cup in 1973-74 and 1979-80 and won the Football League Trophy in 1987-88. The squad captured the FA Charity/Community Shield in 1959; shared it in 1949, 1954, and 1960; and lost it in 1958.

8. The side beat Everton 1-0 in the 1892-93 FA Cup final, downed Newcastle United 3-1 in 1907-08, beat Leicester

City 3-1 in 1948-49, and shut out Blackburn Rovers 3-0 in 1959-60. They were blanked 3-0 by Preston North End in 1888-89, edged 2-1 by Sheffield Wednesday in 1895-96, blanked 1-0 by Tottenham Hotspur in 1920-21, and trounced 4-1 by Portsmouth in 1938-39.

9. Wolves claimed the League Cup in 1973-74 by downing Manchester City 2-1 and won it in 1979-80 by edging Nottingham Forest 1-0. They won the Football League Trophy (Associate Members' Cup) in 1987-88 with a 2-0 decision over Burnley. The team won the FA Charity/ Community Shield in 1959 3-1 over Nottingham Forest. They shared it in 1949, 1954, and 1960 by drawing 1-1 with Portsmouth, 4-4 with West Bromwich Albion, and 2-2 with Burnley. They lost the match 4-1 to Bolton Wanderers in 1958.

10. The club has been relegated 11 times as of 2020-21. They dropped from the top-tier First Division to the Second Division after the 1905-06, 1964-65, 1975-76, 1981-82, and 1983-84 seasons. They fell from the top-tier Premier League to the second-tier Championship League following the 2003-04 and 2011-12 campaigns. They dropped from the second-tier Second Division to the third-tier Third Division North after the 1922-23 season and to the Third Division following 1984-85. They then fell from the Third Division to the fourth-tier Fourth Division the following season. The last time they were relegated was after the 2012-13 season when they dropped from the second-tier Championship League to third-tier League One.

CHAPTER 11:

EUROPE & BEYOND

QUIZ TIME!

1. What was the first major European competition Wolves participated in?

    a. European Cup Winners' Cup

    b. Texaco Cup

    c. UEFA Cup

    d. European Cup

2. Wolverhampton never participated in the UEFA Intertoto Cup.

    a. True

    b. False

3. What was the first team Wolves played against in a major UEFA tournament?

    a. FC Barcelona

    b. FK Austria Wien

    c. Red Star Belgrade

    d. FC Schalke 04

4. How many games has Wolverhampton played in major UEFA tournaments as of 2019-20?

    a. 62
    b. 56
    c. 49
    d. 35

5. Wolves reached which round of the 2019-20 UEFA Europa League?

    a. Round of 16
    b. Quarterfinals
    c. Semifinals
    d. Finals

6. What was the first season the side participated in a major UEFA competition?

    a. 1970-71
    b. 1964-65
    c. 1960-61
    d. 1958-59

7. Wolverhampton has played in five UEFA Cup/Europa League tournaments as of 2020.

    a. True
    b. False

8. Which team did Wolves play in the 1970-71 Texaco Cup final?

    a. Tottenham Hotspur
    b. Derry City FC

c. Hearts of Midlothian FC

d. Motherwell FC

9. How many games has Wolverhampton won in major UEFA tournaments as of 2020?

a. 13

b. 28

c. 30

d. 45

10. Which minor pre-season tournament did Wolves win in 2018?

a. Florida Cup

b. Joan Gamper Trophy

c. Audi Cup

d. Uhrencup

11. Wolves did NOT play which club on their way to the 1971-72 UEFA Cup final?

a. FC Carl Zeiss Jena

b. AC Milan

c. Ferencvárosi TC

d. Juventus

12. Wolverhampton was associated with the Los Angeles Wolves in the inaugural season of the United Soccer Association in 1967.

a. True

b. False

13. How many goals has Wolves scored in major UEFA tournaments as of 2020?

    a. 97
    b. 88
    c. 82
    d. 74

14. What was the result of Wolverhampton's first European Cup match?

    a. 0-0 draw
    b. 0-3 loss
    c. 1-0 win
    d. 2-2 draw

15. Which side did Wolves face in the 1971-72 UEFA Cup final?

    a. Tottenham Hotspur
    b. Paris Saint-Germain
    c. Real Madrid
    d. FC Barcelona

16. Wolverhampton participated in the 2009-10 MLS All-Star Game in North America.

    a. True
    b. False

17. How many matches has Wolves lost in major UEFA tournaments as of 2020?

    a. 20
    b. 16

c. 13

d. 10

18. Which round did Wolves reach in the 1980-81 UEFA Cup tournament?

    a. Semifinals

    b. Quarterfinals

    c. Second round

    d. First round

19. Which team eliminated Wolves in the 2019-20 UEFA Europa League?

    a. RCD Espanyol

    b. Sevilla FC

    c. PSV Eindhoven

    d. Borussia Dortmund

20. Wolverhampton's biggest victory in a European competition was 5-0 against FK Austria Wien.

    a. True

    b. False

QUIZ ANSWERS

1. D – European Cup

2. A – True

3. D – FC Schalke 04

4. C – 49

5. B – Quarterfinals

6. D – 1958-59

7. A – True

8. C – Hearts of Midlothian FC

9. B – 28

10. D – Uhrencup

11. B – AC Milan

12. A – True

13. A – 97

14. D – 2-2 draw

15. A – Tottenham Hotspur

16. B – False

17. C – 13

18. D – First round

19. B – Sevilla FC

20. A – True

DID YOU KNOW?

1. Wolverhampton's first entry into European competitions came in the 1958-59 European Cup. They also played in the 1959-60 European Cup; the 1971-72, 1973-74, and 1974-75 UEFA Cup; and the 1960-61 European Cup Winners' Cup. Their latest appearance in UEFA tournaments was the 2019-20 Europa League. The side also competed in the non-UEFA Texaco Cup in 1970-71.

2. The club's first trip to the continent in the 1958-59 European Cup/Champions League saw them lose 4-3 on aggregate to Schalke 04 of Germany in the first round. They drew 2-2 at home and were edged 2-1 away.

3. The team was back in the European Cup the following season, 1959-60, and made it to the quarterfinals. They downed German side FC Frankfurt 3-2 on aggregate in the preliminary round after winning 2-0 at home and losing 2-1 away. They then beat Red Star Belgrade of Serbia 4-1 on aggregate with a 3-0 home victory and a 1-1 away draw. They met Spanish giants Barcelona in the quarterfinals and were hammered 9-2 on aggregate following a 5-2 home loss and a 4-0 away defeat.

4. The 1960-61 European Cup Winners' Cup resulted in a 5-2 triumph over Austria Wien in the quarterfinals thanks to a 5-0 home win and a 2-0 away loss. Wolves then faced Glasgow Rangers of Scotland in the final four but were

111

eliminated 3-1 on aggregate after a 1-1 home draw and 2-0 away defeat.

5. The 1971-72 UEFA Cup saw Wolves go all the way to the final. They thumped Académica of Portugal 7-1 on aggregate in the first round and Dutch club ADO Den Haag by the same result in the second round. Wolves got past Carl Zeiss Jena of East Germany 4-0 on aggregate in the third round and then edged Italian giants Juventus 3-2 on aggregate in the quarterfinals. They edged Ferencvárosi of Hungary 4-3 in the semifinals to set up an all-English clash against Tottenham Hotspur in the final. However, they were beaten 3-2 on aggregate after a 2-1 home loss and 1-1 away draw.

6. Wolves returned to the UEFA Cup in 1973-74, 1974-75, and 1980-81 but didn't last long in any of the competitions. They beat Belenenses of Portugal 4-1 in the first round in 1973-74 but were then eliminated in the second round after losing on the away-goals rule to Lokomotive Leipzig of East Germany following a 4-4 aggregate result. Wolves won 4-1 at home but lost 3-1 on the road.

7. In the 1974-75 UEFA Cup, Wolves were edged 5-4 on aggregate by Porto of Portugal after winning 3-1 at home but losing 4-1 away. In the 1980-81 tournament, they were eliminated 3-2 on aggregate by Dutch side PSV Eindhoven thanks to a 1-0 home victory and 3-1 away defeat.

8. In the 2019-20 Europa League, Wolves played 17 games as they made it to the quarterfinals. They beat Crusaders FC

of Northern Ireland 6-1 on aggregate in the second qualifying round and FC Pyunik of Armenia 8-0 on aggregate in the third qualifying stage. They qualified for the tournament by downing Torino of Italy 5-3 on aggregate to wind up in Group K with Braga of Portugal, Beşiktaş of Turkey, and Slovan Bratislava of Slovakia.

9. In the 2019-20 Europa League group stage, Wolves lost to Braga 1-0 at home and drew 3-3 away, beat Beşiktaş 4-0 at home and 1-0 away, and downed Slovan Bratislava 1-0 at home and 2-0 away to finish second in Group K. They then beat Espanyol of Spain 6-3 on aggregate in the round of 32 and Olympiacos of Greece 2-1 on aggregate in the round of 16. Wolves faced Sevilla of Spain in the last eight and were edged 1-0 in Germany on an 88th minute goal. Sevilla then went on to win the title.

10. The Texaco Cup was a non-UEFA tournament involving clubs from England, Scotland, and Ireland that didn't qualify for UEFA competitions. The Republic of Ireland and Northern Irish clubs withdrew from the event following the 1971-72 season. Wolves won the 1970-71 Texaco Cup by beating Scottish side Heart of Midlothian 3-2 on aggregate.

CHAPTER 12:

TOP SCORERS

QUIZ TIME!

1. Who is Wolverhampton's all-time leading goal scorer?

   a. Steve Bull

   b. John Richards

   c. Johnny Hancocks

   d. Billy Hartill

2. Wolverhampton has had 13 players win a Golden Boot award as of 2020.

   a. True

   b. False

3. Who was the first player to lead Wolves in scoring in the Football League?

   a. John Brodie

   b. Harry Wood

   c. Joe Cooper

   d. Tommy Knight

4. How many goals did Diogo Jota score in the 2017-18 Championship League season?

    a. 12
    b. 15
    c. 17
    d. 23

5. Who is Wolverhampton's top scorer in the Premier League as of 2019-20?

    a. Raúl Jiménez
    b. Diogo Jota
    c. Ivan Cavaleiro
    d. Bright Enobakhare

6. How many goals did Johnny Hancocks tally in all competitions for the team?

    a. 182
    b. 177
    c. 167
    d. 157

7. Henri Camara led the squad with seven goals in its first season in the Premier League in 2003-04.

    a. True
    b. False

8. Who led the 2008-09 domestic league season with 25 goals?

    a. Sylvan Ebanks-Blake
    b. Chris Iwelumo

   c. Michael Kightly

   d. Sam Vokes

9. How many goals did Steven Fletcher notch in the 2011-12 domestic league season?

   a. 7

   b. 9

   c. 12

   d. 15

10. Who led the top-flight in scoring in 1946-47 with 38 goals?

   a. Tom Phillipson

   b. Jimmy Murray

   c. Steve Bull

   d. Dennis Westcott

11. Which player scored 15 goals in the 2014-15 domestic league season?

   a. Nouha Dicko

   b. Benik Afobe

   c. David Edwards

   d. Bakary Sako

12. Steve Bull tallied a total of 18 hat-tricks in all competitions with Wolverhampton.

   a. True

   b. False

13. How many goals did John Richards contribute in all competitions with the side?

a. 215

b. 194

c. 181

d. 175

14. Which two players led the team with 10 goals each in the 2016-17 domestic league?

    a. Ivan Cavaleiro and Nouha Dicko

    b. Danny Batth and Hélder Costa

    c. Matt Doherty and Ivan Cavaleiro

    d. Hélder Costa and David Edwards

15. How many goals did Steve Bull rack up in all competitions in 1987-88?

    a. 44

    b. 47

    c. 52

    d. 56

16. Billy Hartill holds the club record for most goals scored in the top-flight, with 158.

    a. True

    b. False

17. Who led the team with 19 goals in the 2004-05 domestic league?

    a. Carl Cort

    b. Kenny Miller

    c. Leon Clarke

    d. Kevin Cooper

18. How many goals did Steve Bull score for Wolves in all competitions?

   a. 260
   b. 285
   c. 306
   d. 313

19. Who led Wolverhampton with 21 goals in all competitions in 2001-02?

   a. Alex Rae
   b. Shaun Newton
   c. Nathan Blake
   d. Dean Sturridge

20. Robbie Keane led Wolves in scoring in three seasons from 1996-97 to 1998-99.

   a. True
   b. False

QUIZ ANSWERS

1. A – Steve Bull

2. B – False

3. B – Harry Wood

4. C – 17

5. A – Raúl Jiménez

6. C – 167

7. A – True

8. A – Sylvan Ebanks-Blake

9. C – 12

10. D – Dennis Westcott

11. D – Bakary Sako

12. A – True

13. B – 194

14. D – Hélder Costa and David Edwards

15. C – 52

16. B – False

17. B – Kenny Miller

18. C – 306

19. D – Dean Sturridge

20. B – False

DID YOU KNOW?

1. As of April 2021, the top 15 scorers in Wolves history are: Steve Bull, 306; John Richards, 194; Billy Hartill, 170; Johnny Hancocks, 167; Jimmy Murray, 166; Peter Broadbent, 145; Harry Wood, 126; Dennis Westcott, 124; Derek Dougan, 123; Roy Swinbourne, 114; Kenny Hibbitt, 114; Dennis Wilshaw, 113; Jimmy Mullen, 112; Tom Phillipson, 111; and Andy Mutch, 106.

2. The current club record for most goals in a season in all competitions is held by Steve Bull with 52 in 1987-88 in the Fourth Division. The most league goals tallied in one season is 38 by Dennis Westcott in the First Division in 1946-47. The most career goals scored in the top-flight is 158 by Johnny Hancocks between 1946 and 1957, and the most goals netted in European competition is 12 by Derek Dougan between 1967 and 1975.

3. Steve Bull also holds the current record for the most career hat-tricks with the club at 18 between 1986 and 1999. The record for most goals scored in one match, five, is shared by several players. Joe Butcher was the first to achieve it against Accrington on November 19, 1892, in the First Division. Tom Phillipson did it against Bradford City on December 25, 1926, in the Second Division. Billy Hartill managed it twice, against Notts County on October 12, 1929, in the Second Division and against Aston Villa on September 3, 1934, in the First Division.

4. When it comes to club scoring, the most league goals Wolves has scored in a season is 115 in the Second Division in 1931-32. The fewest league goals tallied is 27 in the First Division in 1983-84. The most league goals conceded in a season is 99 in the First Division in 1905-06. The fewest league goals conceded in a season is 27 in the Third Division in 1923-24. The most goals scored in a league game is 10 against Leicester City in the First Division in 1938, and the most goals in a cup contest is 14 against Crosswell's Brewery in the second round of the FA Cup in 1886.

5. Steve Bull notched 306 goals in 561 appearances for Wolves to be crowned the club's all-time leading scorer, with 250 of them coming in league play, which is a club record. His 52 goals in a season and 18 career hat-tricks are also Wolves high marks. Bull joined from West Bromwich Albion in 1986 when the side was in the Fourth Division and remained until 1999. He helped the team win the Fourth Division and Third Division titles in successive seasons in 1987-88 and 1988-89, as well as the 1987-88 Football League Trophy. He was named the team's Player of the Year three times, became the only player to score at least 50 goals for an English League club in successive seasons, and led the team in scoring for eight straight seasons. He also scored four goals in 13 outings with the English senior side.

6. Until Steve Bull came along, fellow Wolves Hall of Fame member John Richards was the team's top goal-getter

with 194 in 485 appearances. He formed an effective partnership with Derek Dougan and helped the side reach the 1971-72 UEFA Cup final. He scored a career-best 36 goals the next season and led the squad in scoring for eight seasons. Nicknamed "King John," Richards started his career with the club and remained until joining Marítimo of Portugal in 1983. He scored the winning goal for Wolves in the 1973-74 League Cup final, won the cup again six years later, and helped the team win the Second Division title in 1976-77. Richards scored a club-high 24 FA Cup goals during his career and later served as a director and managing director of the club.

7. Northern Ireland international forward and Wolves Hall of Fame member Derek Dougan joined the club for a £50,000 fee from Leicester City in March 1967. He helped the side earn promotion out of the Second Division in 1966-67 by finishing as runner-up as well as lifting the 1970-71 Texaco Cup and the 1973-74 League Cup. He also played in the 1971-72 UEFA Cup final. Dougan netted 123 goals in 323 Wolves matches, led the side in scoring in three seasons, and scored a hat-trick in his home debut. He also played in America while with Wolves and left in 1975 for Kettering Town. Dougan was once the chairman of the PFA footballers' union, and, after becoming a TV pundit, he returned to the club as chief executive.

8. Center-forward Dennis Westcott joined Wolves in 1936 from New Brighton and stayed until joining Blackburn Rovers in 1948. His Hall of Fame tenure with the club was

interrupted by World War II, but he helped the team win the Football League War Cup in 1941-42. After the conflict, he scored a club-record 38 league goals in 1946-47. Before the war, Westcott tallied 43 goals in all competitions in 1938-39 to help the side finish runner-up in the First Division and FA Cup and as First Division runner-up the previous campaign. He scored 124 times in 144 matches for the club and led it in scoring for three seasons. Westcott passed away from leukemia in 1960 just after turning 43 years old.

9. Roy Swinbourne joined Wolves as a youth player just as World War II came to an end and went on to notch 114 goals in 230 contests with the senior side between 1949 and 1957 when he retired due to a knee injury. He scored 17 goals in the first 11 games in 1955-56, including three straight hat-tricks. Swinbourne led the team in goals with 22 in 1950-51 and 21 in 1952-53, but his most productive campaign was 1953-54 when he scored 24 goals to help the club win its first First Division title. He scored both goals in a 2-0 victory over Tottenham Hotspur in the final game of the season to clinch the trophy and is a member of Wolverhampton's Hall of Fame.

10. Another Wolves Hall of Fame member and top-10 scorer was midfielder Kenny Hibbitt, who joined the side from Bradford Park Avenue in 1968 as a teenager. He led the side in goals in 1974-75 with 17, which included nine from the penalty spot and all four goals in a 4-2 victory over Newcastle United. He played in the 1971-72 UEFA Cup

final, scored in the 1973-74 League Cup final triumph, and won the League Cup again in 1979-80. Hibbitt contributed 114 goals in 574 appearances, which ranks second all-time in games played for the team. He joined Coventry City in 1984 on a free transfer.

CONCLUSION

Wolves has been roaming UK soccer pitches since 1877, and you've just read through the amazing history of the club. We hope we've presented the Wolverhampton Wanderers' story to you in comprehensive and entertaining trivia form, and it's all the better if you learned something new about the club along the way.

Outfitted with a dozen unique, quiz-filled chapters, and a mixed bag of "Did You Know?" facts, you should now be well prepared to challenge fellow Wolves and soccer fans to an assortment of quiz contests to determine who the top dog is.

We've included as many of the club's top players and managers as possible and provided a wide range of informative and educational facts concerning its successes, disappointments, transfers, and records. We apologize if we've left your favorites out of the book, but with such a long history, it's impossible to include every club member.

We hope you'll be inclined to share this trivia and fact book with others to help teach Wolverhampton's intriguing history to those who may not be aware of it.

The ongoing Wolves story is quite remarkable in many ways, and we'd like to take this opportunity to thank you for being a loyal and passionate fan of the club.

Printed in Great Britain
by Amazon

44691051R00076